A Cub Scout from Greater London Middlesex West battles against an obstacle, and tries not to spill a cup of water, on a County Activity Day.

Tim Quin, of the 7th Hounslow, learns the skill of basket weaving during Cub Camp.

photographs: © Dave Wood

The Official Cub Scout Annual of The Scout Association

Scouts

This book belongs to:

Randal Karsten
Merry Christmas
from
Alex Chalmers

of the

Cub Scout Pack

£4.99
UK only

Not your 'run of the mill' mill

"It is perfectly delightful here, and I am getting on with my writing very well – being entirely my own master – and very quiet sitting out in the garden all day."

text: Mike Brennan

The above passage is taken from a letter which Baden-Powell wrote to his mother on 16 July 1907. The 'writing' to which B.-P. referred was, of course, *Scouting for Boys*. The 'here' was the Mill House on Wimbledon Common. Although B.-P. spent his time working on the book in many different locations, we know from his letters and diaries of the time that it was at Wimbledon windmill (in south London) where he worked on the final copy of what was to be the first edition of *Scouting for Boys*.

Wimbledon windmill – its early history

Built by Charles March, a local carpenter, in 1817, Wimbledon windmill is believed to be the only remaining example in this country of what is known as a 'hollow post-mill'. Post-mills first appeared in this country around the year 1180, the name coming from the fact that the mill consisted of a small building balanced on a central post. The post acted as a pivot so that the whole building and its sails could be turned around to face the wind. Post-mills were most common in Holland and were rather rare in Britain.

The fact that Charles March was a carpenter and not a millwright (a millwright was a person who built mills) may explain why he chose to build such an unusual windmill at Wimbledon. At the time when he decided to build his mill, there was a strikingly similar mill situated at nearby Southwark. It is quite possible that Charles March copied this building not knowing that this was not a 'normal' English windmill.

Wimbledon windmill was used for grinding corn to make flour. It worked as a corn grinding mill until the 1860s when it went out of business as more efficient water-powered mills in the Thames Valley came into widespread use. Wimbledon windmill was then converted for living in but, through neglect, fell into disrepair until 1893 when the Conservators of Wimbledon Common raised funds and began to restore it to good condition.

Below: *Wimbledon windmill, photographed in 1955. When used as a mill for grinding corn, the top part of the mill building spun around to catch the wind in its sails. Mills that could spin around were known as post-mills because they rotated around a central post. The earliest windmills of this type were built over 800 years ago and their central posts were often tree trunks. Wimbledon windmill was converted to living accommodation in the last century, and it was here in 1907–08 that Robert Baden-Powell wrote parts of his famous Scouting for Boys.*

Below left: *This is how Wimbledon windmill looked in 1825, just eight years after Charles March had built it. Note the circular stone leaning against the mill. Inside the mill were several of these large stones which crushed corn to make flour.*

© The Scout Association

Wimbledon windmill and Scouting

As far as Scouting is concerned, the important year in the mill's history is 1908, the year of the first publication of *Scouting for Boys*. Baden-Powell's diary entry for 26 December 1907 reads: *"Went into residence at Mill House"* (in other words, Wimbledon windmill).

A letter from B.-P. dated 30 December 1907 contains the passage: *"All goes well here. I am working hard – enjoying frequent walks between whiles in this splendid air"*. It is believed that the final draft of *Scouting for Boys* was completed at Wimbledon windmill in 1908.

It was not until forty years later, however, that the windmill's significance in the history of Scouting was formally recognised. On 5 June 1948, Sir Percy Everett (Deputy Chief Scout at that time) unveiled a commemorative plaque to mark the fortieth anniversary of the completion of *Scouting for Boys*. To this day, the plaque remains over the door to the windmill marking the site of this much neglected piece of Scouting history.

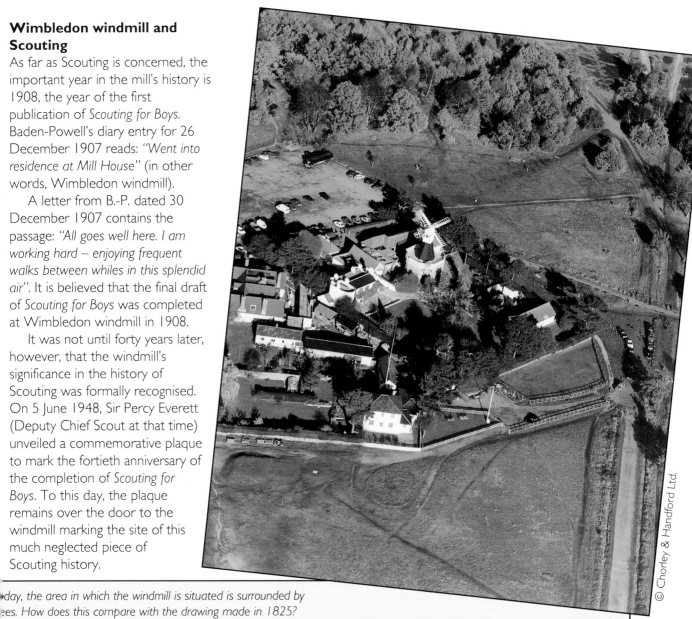

© Chorley & Handford Ltd.

...day, the area in which the windmill is situated is surrounded by ...ees. How does this compare with the drawing made in 1825?

TYPES OF WINDMILL

Post-mill

The big problem with post-mills (such as Wimbledon windmill) was that working conditions inside them were very cramped as all the machinery had to be housed in the moving body of the mill. The problem of cramped conditions was solved with other types of windmill, such as the tower-mill and the smock-mill.

Tower-mill

With the tower-mill, the mill's sails were carried on a rotating cap which sat on top of the main building which was made from brick.

Smock-mill

In areas where brick was scarce, mill towers were often built from timber, with the tower raised from the ground on a small brick base to protect the timber from rot. These mills became known as smock-mills.

illustrations: Rick Blackely

5

*W*hen you are a Cub Scout, one of the many badges you can work towards is the Health and Fitness Activity badge. This requires you to be moderately fit but mainly to know about how to get and stay fit and healthy. One way is to take regular exercise. That means small amounts of exercise, and often.

Here, we provide you with an easy way to get yourself fit and stay healthy by following a series of exercises and games which will make exercise fun to do.

LET'S GET PHYSICAL!

Am I fit and healthy?

If you can actually do some of the following challenges and not feel bad after them, then your body is fit. If your body is in good working order and you feel able to tackle a new challenge, then you are healthy. Regular exercise helps your body in three ways. It affects how well your muscles work (strength), your ability to keep going (stamina) and keeps your body flexible (suppleness).

Why bother to keep fit and healthy?

For one thing, you will be less likely to go down with the dreaded lergy and get a nasty cold; you will look better because your hair, skin and how your whole body looks improve as organs and your body chemicals function better; and finally, you will feel better as you will have more energy to do more things.

"I am what I eat"

This is a very famous saying. Basically, it means that if you eat lots of fatty foods, you will end up being over weight, but if you eat lots of healthy food, you will be healthy. For our body to work, we need the right chemicals and we get these from eating the right foods and doing the right exercise.

Here's the best way to have a healthy diet...

✔ Make sure that most of your food is fresh and not tinned or frozen. Fresh food has more vitamins.

✔ Cut down on animal fats by drinking skimmed milk and eating low fat cheese and white meat and fish, rather than red meat. Replace butter with margarine. Don't eat more than three eggs a week.

✔ Avoid frying food.

✔ Increase your fibre intake by eating wholemeal bread, cereals and pasta and eating brown, instead of white rice.

Warm up exercises

Before doing exercises, you must warm your muscles up gradually. That means gently stretching arm, leg, waist and neck muscles using a series of bends and stretches.

Side Stretch
A basic warm up exercise. Hold hands above head and bend slowly sideways at the waist. Hold. Repeat to other side.

Trunk stretch
Hold hands in front of chest. Feet apart. Turn head and body to one side. Repeat to other side.

Calf and hip stretch
Keep back upright. Lean back from waist and press hips downwards. Hold, then repeat.

text: Ron Crabb   illustrations: Clive Spong

A fitness plan

Use the chart below to work out your own fitness plan. The shaded boxes show how often you should exercise each week. You will see that the activities are split up into 'stretching', 'building stamina', 'strength building' and 'playing games'. A list of what you can do for these headings is shown here to the right.

Remember, it is always important to warm up before you do exercises and to warm down afterwards by doing a few stretching exercises. Take it easy, don't go silly and if you start to feel so out of breath that you can't talk to someone whilst exercising, you are pushing yourself too hard. Over a few weeks' of following this plan, you will feel much better.

Stretching
Do the warm ups and really loosen up your muscles and joints.

Stamina
Badminton
Basketball
Cycling
Dancing
Football (rugby and soccer)
Gymnastics
Brisk walking
Hockey
Jogging
Netball
Rowing
Running
Skating (roller and ice)
Skiing (cross-country)
Skipping
Squash
Swimming
Tennis

Strength
Badminton
Boxing
Canoeing
Fencing
Football (rugby and soccer)
Gymnastics
Hockey
Horse-riding
Judo
Netball
Rowing
Running
Sailing
Skating (roller and ice)
Squash
Swimming
Tennis

Games
This simply means active games and sports which you can play with friends from school or elsewhere in your spare time.

Time spent per session	10 minutes of stretching	30 minutes building stamina	30 minutes building strength	1 hour playing games
Day 1	▓ shaded	▓ shaded		
Day 2	▓ shaded		▓ shaded	
Day 3	▓ shaded			
Day 4	▓ shaded			
Day 5	▓ shaded		▓ shaded	
Day 6	▓ shaded			▓ shaded
Day 7	▓ shaded	▓ shaded		

CRASH, BANG, WALLOP!

Next time you watch television, turn the sound right down. What do you notice is missing (apart from the voices, of course!)? It's the sound effects such as the crashes, bangs, roars, hums, whooshes and so on. We hear them all the time on radio and TV – *so here's how you can make your very own.*

Sound effect
★ A fish, a diver underwater, a magic potion boiling up, food cooking – even a ship sinking!

How to make it
Blow through a straw into a tumbler of water, making lots of bubbles.

Sound effect
★ Volcano erupting or a clap of thunder.

How to make it
Hold a large tin tray and 'shake' it, holding both sides.

Sound effect
★ A car back-firing, an explosion, something popping or a gun firing.

How to make it
Blow up an empty crisp packet. Clap your hands with the crisp packet between them and the packet should burst.

Sound effect
★ A river or the sea.

How to make it
Fill a washing-up bowl with water. Swish your hand or hands around from side to side.

Sound effect
★ A dinosaur wading through a swamp or people walking through deep water or the sea.

How to make it
Hold a small tin of baked beans in each hand. Plunge one tin into a bowl of water, then the other.

Sound effect
★ Something heavy falling into the sea – or a man overboard!

How to make it
Drop a tin of baked beans into a bucket of water.

text: Brenda Apsley   illustrations: Andy Robb

Sound effect

★ Something small falling into a river or a lake – or even a witch's cauldron of boiling liquid!

How to make it

Drop a pebble or marble into a bowl of water.

Sound effect

★ Horses' hooves.

How to make it

Beat your hands on the side of a table in a regular rhythm. The louder and faster the beats, the nearer the horses are.

Sound effect

★ Feet walking across pebbles or shingle on the beach.

How to make it

Put some dried pasta shapes or peas on to a tin tray. Holding a tin of baked beans in each hand, press down into the dried peas, first one hand, then the other.

You and a friend can put these sound effects to good use in this short play.

Smugglers at Stormy Cove
Scene: a dark, moonlit night

	Speech	Sound effect
		Thunderclaps
Jake:	What a night for smuggling!	
Will:	Yeah. Help me with this chest.	Heavy chest being dragged across shingle; footsteps in the shingle
Jake:	Got it.	Horses' hooves
Will:	The customs men! Quick!	Rifle shot bangs
Jake:	There's the boat. Heave!	Sounds of the sea; smugglers wade out
Will:	Nearly there.	Small plop in the water
Jake:	My lucky doubloon!	Horses' hooves closer; rifle shots
Will:	Leave it! Help me get this chest aboard.	Rifle shots; thunderclap
Jake:	That's my good luck gone! I've got to…	Hand swishes in water
Will:	No, Jake! I can't hold the chest on my own!	Horses' hooves louder
Jake:	Just a…	Chest falls into sea
Will:	Oh, no! They're getting closer!	Rifle shots

To be continued…

Do the customs men catch the two smugglers? What happens to the treasure chest? You decide how the play ends – *and don't forget the sound effects!*

Make a periscope

Have you ever been in a crowd at a football match or other sporting event and wished you were just that little bit taller so you could see the action more clearly? Perhaps it was at a pop concert or a public event such as a parade. A simple home-made periscope could be the answer to your wish!

You will need...

- ◆ 2 mirrors, approximately 10cm x 11.5cm
- ◆ A sheet of stiff card 50cm square
- ◆ A pair of scissors
- ◆ A pencil
- ◆ A ruler
- ◆ Glue (suitable for gluing the mirrors to the card)
- ◆ Strong sticky tape

This is what you do...

1 Using the diagram as a guide, draw the shape on to your card and cut it out.
2 Fold along the lines and, using the sticky tape, tape where the edges meet to form a long oblong tube with a hole near the top of one side and another near the bottom of the other side.
3 Take one of the mirrors and stick it into place at a 45° angle as shown in the diagram.
4 Take the second mirror and adjust the position as necessary before sticking it into place.

If you are successful at making this cardboard periscope, you could try adapting the dimensions and making a more permanent wooden version.

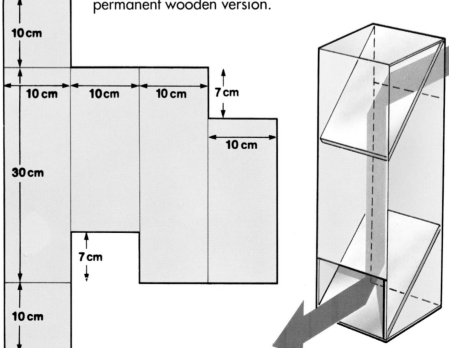

text: Mike Brennan   illustrations: Rick Blackely

This is what you do...

❶ Take the empty can and ask an adult to supervise you whilst you cut it in half. Use one of the halves to cut a strip of metal from the can. File off any rough or sharp edges. The strip needs to be 2–3cm wide and 10–12cm long.

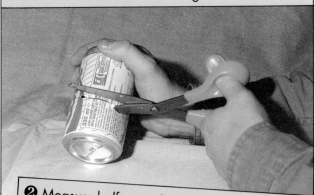

❷ Measure half way along the strip and prick a hole in it with the drawing pin. Make sure the metal strip is resting on a hard surface.

❸ Bend the strip into a U shape and fix it to the bottom of the glass using the sticky tape.

A useful tip

If the object you are viewing is out of focus, you will need to adjust the height of the metal strip on the glass. Experiment until you have the distance set correctly and you will find that the magnified image can be seen clearly.

Let's make... a water-drop microscope

Here's how to make a microscope from everyday objects you'll find at home.

You will need...

- ✔ An empty aluminium drinks can
- ✔ A large drawing pin
- ✔ An old pair of scissors
- ✔ A glass tumbler
- ✔ Sticky tape
- ✔ A small torch
- ✔ A couple of books to rest the glass on

❹ Switch the torch on and place it under the glass. Use the books to give the glass a bit more height if the torch is too long.

❺ Place a drop of water on to the pin hole using the handle of a teaspoon (or something similar). This will act as the lens of the microscope and will magnify whatever you look at. Try to keep the drop of water as small as possible so that it just covers the hole.

❻ Place whatever you want to study on the bottom of the glass and look at it through the water drop.

text: Peter Barker   photographs: Dave Smith

How good a Cub are you?

Try our fun quiz to see for yourself just how good a Cub Scout you really are – and how prepared you are in an emergency. Then test your friends too.

text: Emma Wood   illustrations: Andy Robb

1
You are sitting on a bus and you find a five pound note tucked down the side of the seat. Would you…
A Keep it and buy some sweets or a present for someone?
B Pick it up but put it in a charity collecting box when you get off the bus?
C Give it to the driver or conductor?

2
You are in the countryside and you come across an empty field with a gate that has been left open. Would you…
A Shut it straight away?
B Leave it as it is in case a farmer wanted it left open?
C Report it to the police?

3
You are walking by a canal and you see that a child has fallen in. Would you…
A Jump in and try to rescue him?
B Grab a long stick, lie down and try to reach him?
C Quickly try to teach him how to swim by shouting and doing the arm and leg movements?

4
You are in a hurry to get to Cubs and are dashing out of a shop when you see a number of people about to come in through the swing doors. Do you…
A Stop and hold the door open for them?
B Rush through and say you're sorry?
C Try and find another door which isn't so crowded?

12

5

You are playing a game at Cubs when the Cub you are playing against cheats in order to win. Do you…
A Ignore it as it's only a game?
B Cheat yourself to make it fair?
C Stop the game and tell Akela?

6

You see a friend of yours stealing a bar of chocolate from a sweetshop. Would you…
A Tell the shopkeeper?
B Tell your friend and get him to go back and pay for it?
C Keep quiet and do nothing?

7

You are in your tent at camp and the other members of your Six start planning to let down all of the other tents. Would you…
A Join in as it's good fun?
B Tell them that it could be dangerous if poles and canvas fell on people?
C Run outside and wake everyone to warn them?

8

You are walking along a street and you see smoke coming from the windows of a house. First, would you…
A Stop and watch to see how well the firemen put it out when they arrive?
B Knock on the door to make sure nobody is inside, then phone for the fire brigade?
C Run home to tell your parents?

9

You are visiting your grandma on your own and she falls over and hurts her leg. Do you…
A Dial 999 and ask for the ambulance service?
B Sit with her until someone arrives who can help?
C Give her some brandy to cheer her up?

10

You are playing in a park and you come across a bird which has obviously injured its wing. Would you…
A Leave it where it is as it will probably die anyway?
B Wrap a handkerchief around it, pick it up and ask a vet, policeman or your parents to help?
C Put it into a litter bin so that nobody treads on it?

SCORING			
Look to see how many points you scored for each of your answers:			
1	A = 0	B = 3	C = 5
2	A = 3	B = 5	C = 0
3	A = 0	B = 5	C = 0
4	A = 5	B = 1	C = 0
5	A = 5	B = 0	C = 2
6	A = 2	B = 5	C = 0
7	A = 0	B = 5	C = 1
8	A = 0	B = 5	C = 2
9	A = 5	B = 2	C = 0
10	A = 1	B = 5	C = 0

HOW MANY DID YOU SCORE?

under 20	Not very good at all. Maybe you spend most of your Pack Meetings asleep! Try the quiz again and think a bit more carefully about your answers.
21–34	Not bad. Perhaps you need to read your Cub Scout Handbook and this Annual again to help you become better prepared for things.
35–44	Well done. You made some very good decisions and are well on the way to being a top Cub Scout!
45–50	Congratulations! You are a first class Cub Scout. If you scored 50 out of 50, you are obviously prepared for any emergency.

☆Get☆ cooking! ☆ ☆ ☆

Eggy Nests

For each nest you will need...
- ☆ 2 slices of bread
- ☆ Margarine
- ☆ 1 egg
- ☆ 1 slice of ham or, if you do not eat meat, 1 cheese slice
- ☆ Salt
- ☆ A grown-up to help you!

This is what you do...

❶ Turn on the oven. Set it at gas mark 5, 190°C or 375°F.

text: Brenda Apsley   illustrations: Jeannette Slater

14

❷ Cut a hole in one slice of bread. Use an 8cm pastry cutter or a glass tumbler. Don't break the crusts of bread.

❸ Spread some margarine on the other slice of bread. Put it, margarine side down, on a baking tray. Put the ham or cheese slice on top.

❹ Put the cut slice of bread on top. Spread a little margarine on the 'sandwich'.

❺ Break an egg into a saucer. Careful! Try not to break the yolk. Put the egg into the bread nest. Add a little salt.

❻ Put into the oven. After about 12 minutes the egg should be set. If it is not, bake it for another 2 or 3 minutes.

❼ Ask a grown-up to help you take the nest from the oven – *remember to wear oven gloves.*

Yummy Yoghurt

Follow this recipe to make yoghurt at home.

You will need...

- ☆ 1 pint of milk
- ☆ A carton of plain yoghurt – it must be 'live', so read the label carefully
- ☆ Fruit, honey, nuts or raisins for flavouring

This is what you do...

❶ Pour the milk into a saucepan. Warm it slowly, but do not let it boil. Ask a grown-up to help you.

❷ When the milk is hot, take the pan off the heat. Leave it to cool for 5 minutes – until it is cool enough for you to dip your finger in it.

❸ Pour the milk into a bowl. Add the plain yoghurt. Mix with a spoon.

❹ Cover the bowl with clingfilm. Put it in a warm place – an airing cupboard is ideal.

❺ Leave it for 24 hours (1 day) to thicken up.

❻ After 24 hours the yoghurt should be ready to eat. Now is the time to add your favourite flavouring. Here are some ideas:

☆ **Banana and honey flavour**

Cut a banana into small pieces. Add it to the yoghurt with 2 tablespoons of runny honey. Stir well.

☆ **Berry flavour**

Chop up some strawberries, raspberries (or a mixture of both). Stir into the yoghurt. If you like smooth yoghurt, mash the fruit first

☆ **Peanut butter flavour**

Stir in 3 tablespoons of crunchy peanut butter.

☆ **Nuts and raisins flavour**

Chop up some nuts and raisins. Stir into the yoghurt.

STORY: BRENNAN & FIELDING   ART: ROB SHARP   LETTERING: MIKE TURNER

19

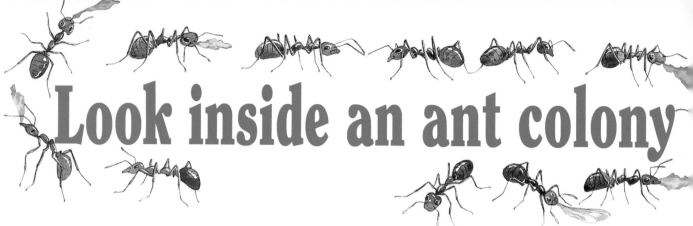

Look inside an ant colony

Most insects live alone, but ants are different. They live in large nests or colonies where each ant has a job to do. The tunnels and 'rooms' of the nest are like a big underground city.

Expert builders

Ants are expert builders and tunnellers. Tiny entrance holes near paths, walls and in soft earth lead down to a maze of tiny passageways and rooms or 'chambers'. The temperature in the ant city is always the same, and inside the ants are safe from enemies such as birds.

The queen

Every nest has one queen ant. She is much bigger than the other ants, and her only job is to lay eggs. She stays inside the nest where she can live for up to fifteen years. Worker ants bring her food. Winged male ants fertilize the eggs. 'Nurse' worker ants look after the eggs. They carry them to special 'nursery' chambers in their jaws, and look after them until they grow and hatch as adult ants. All worker ants are female.

Collecting food

It is the job of other worker ants to collect food. Hunters or scouts set off from the nest. They leave a scent trail that other ants can follow. If hunters find a supply of food, they send a message back to the colony and hundreds of helpers soon arrive to carry the food back to the nest.

Housekeeper ants

These ants store food in 'larder' chambers. Ants eat almost anything – grain, seeds and even meat. Housekeeper ants collect rubbish from inside the colony and take it to deep 'dustbin' tunnels.

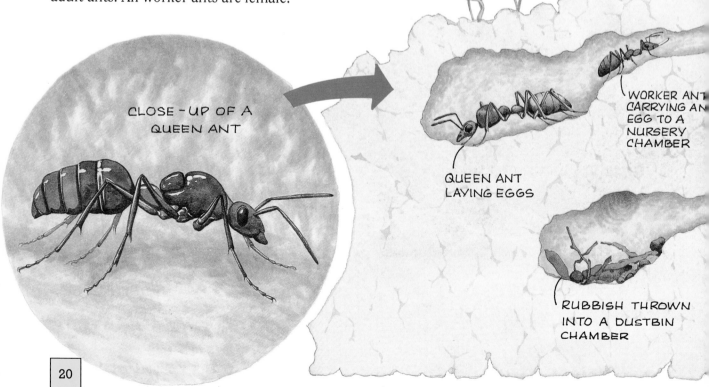

CLOSE-UP OF A QUEEN ANT

WORKER ANT CARRYING AN EGG TO A NURSERY CHAMBER

QUEEN ANT LAYING EGGS

RUBBISH THROWN INTO A DUSTBIN CHAMBER

Living with greenfly

Ants love to eat sweet honeydew. Tiny insects called aphids (greenfly) suck up sweet sap from plants to get the food they need. The sap they do not need oozes from their bodies as honeydew. Ants have learned to look after aphids, just as farmers look after cattle or sheep. The ants protect the aphids from enemies and 'stroke' them so that they release the tasty honeydew.

Garden ants

The brown-black garden ant is the most common in Britain. It has six legs, and is 3 to 5mm long. It is quite good-natured, unlike some larger ants from hotter countries which can bite quite hard. Ants are very strong, and can carry things many times their own weight. Workers can live for up to seven years.

Soldier worker ants

Soldier worker ants protect the colony and fight battles against other ant groups.

Communicating with each other

Ants 'talk' to each other by rubbing their antennae (feelers) together. They pass on messages about where food is to be found, or if there is danger. Young ants learn from older ones.

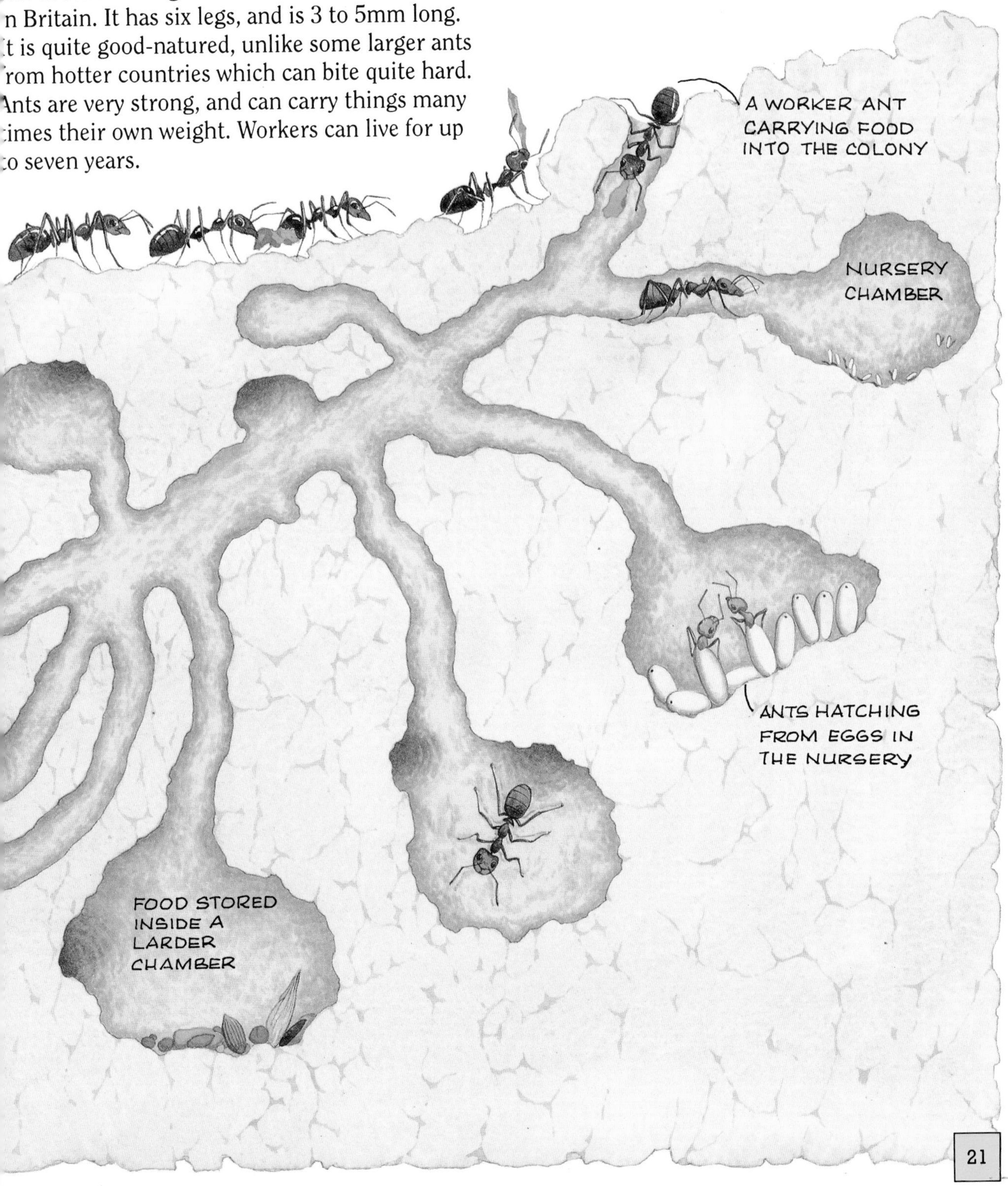

A WORKER ANT CARRYING FOOD INTO THE COLONY

NURSERY CHAMBER

ANTS HATCHING FROM EGGS IN THE NURSERY

FOOD STORED INSIDE A LARDER CHAMBER

text: Brenda Apsley   illustrations: David Webb

21

Adam's Alien Adventure

Adam hurried along the street, pulling Jones his spaniel with him as fast as was possible. Adam was keen to get into town to visit his favourite shop, Maguire's Models, as he had decided to spend his pocket money on one of their best models ever, a really good alien model that he had seen in there a few days before. If he hurried he would have time to buy the model and get home before tea, and he might even have time to start one of the drawings that he did of all his model aliens. He carefully sketched them with brilliant spaceships and planets in the background.

Adam had started collecting models for his Hobbies and Interest badge at Cubs. Since then he had been hooked and had started collecting the special alien models from Maguire's. Adam loved Maguire's which was full of science fiction models and games. He liked to wander around the tiny shop with its glass cases and shelves packed with comics, books and models of all shapes and sizes. The display Adam liked best of all though, was the aliens. They were together in one corner of the shop on lots of shelves and there were all kinds of other bits and pieces to go with the aliens – paint and glue and space stations that looked a bit like Tracey Island and even the odd spaceship.

Today however, Adam noticed a rather unusual spaceship, on a shelf just at his eye level, that he didn't remember seeing before. It looked rather like a strange pod with short, black supports, like legs, sticking out at the bottom. It was leaning at a rather odd angle, as one of the supports appeared to be missing. The strange pod was a funny green

story: Sara Fielding   illustrations: Jan McCafferty

n colour and there was what looked like a tiny trapdoor in the top of it. Adam was about to lose interest in the strange object, as he spotted the new alien he wanted right alongside it, but then he saw an even better model leaning against the new spaceship. It was small but very realistic with a huge golden helmet that completely covered its face and a swirling cloak of all kinds of weird designs. On an impulse, Adam decided to buy it instead, and he began to chat excitedly to the shop owner about what other new aliens would be coming in soon. He was about to pay for his model and go home, when he noticed Jones sitting in front of the broken spaceship and whining excitedly. Curiously, Adam crossed the shop again and picked up the little spaceship. It did feel weird, almost warm to the touch. "What is this Mr Maguire?" he asked the owner. "It feels funny and it seems to be broken."

"Oh that," replied Mr. Maguire. "It's quite strange, I found it outside in the alley when I went to empty the bins and brought it in to fix it, thinking someone had accidentally dropped it. But it's funny, it isn't made of any modelling material that I know of. Why don't you have a go and see what you can do with it?"

Jones kept jumping up and down and whining, so Adam decided to take the ship with him and go home.

Once at home, Adam sat down to eat his beefburgers and chips but for some reason he felt quite distracted and his eyes kept straying over to the strange alien and spaceship. As soon as tea was over, he decided to take his new models to his room and try and fix the broken ship. Some time later, he was still trying. Nothing would stick to the ship's surface, no modelling glue or tape would work. In the end he decided to draw the ship instead. "Look Jones, I'm drawing the ship and I bet it will be easier to draw a new leg for it, than it is to try and stick one on!"

Adam spent quite a long time on his drawing, which turned out to be really quite good. The strange ship looked much better with its brand new support in position, and Adam began carefully to add some colour to his picture, using the crayons he'd had for Christmas.

When his Mum called him to say that it was bedtime, Adam yawned and stretched and decided to finish the picture in the morning. He quickly had a wash, said goodnight and sank into bed, after rather

reluctantly kicking Jones out of his room as he wasn't allowed to sleep upstairs. Sometime later he awoke in the darkness and sat up. What had woken him? In the faint light from the window he could see his picture propped up next to the model ship on his chest of drawers. Both seemed to be faintly glowing but the model alien was nowhere to be seen. That's strange, thought Adam, I'm sure I left it next to the ship.

Hearing a faint scratching outside the door, Adam decided to break the rules, just for once, and let Jones into his room to keep him company. He forgot all about the missing alien model and decided to carry on with his drawing, as he was too wide awake to sleep. He switched on his little reading lamp and set to work. He was soon completely absorbed in his picture and his crayons seemed to fly across the paper with a life of their own. He didn't know what time it was when he finally dropped the last crayon in exhaustion. His picture was brilliant! Glowing with colour the ship sat in a strange landscape with a background of a weird galaxy of suns and moons. Dropping asleep, Adam glanced across at the broken model ship lying in a shaft of moonlight, and thought how great it would be if it looked just like the one in his picture and could really fly through space!

Adam had a strange dream that night. He dreamt that he was woken up again by Jones scratching at the window and making low, growling noises in his throat. Sleepily Adam got up. Outside it was a clear but windy night,

nd the darkness was broken up every so often by the moonlight, which shone quite brightly through gaps in the clouds which scudded across the sky. "What's up Jones?" Adam whispered to his dog who was shivering in excitement. Just then he noticed a movement in the garden below the window, and recognised a small, golden, shimmery object. The ship! What on earth was it doing out there? Adam watched open-mouthed as it began to slowly spin around, perfectly balanced on four supports! Glancing back into his room, Adam saw his picture which lay where the ship had been and it too was glowing in the moonlight, shimmering gold and green. I wonder... he thought as he turned back, just in time to see the tiny craft lift itself off the ground. For one moment, as it swooped towards the house, Adam could see it clearly and as it hovered in front of the window, he felt sure that the little ship contained his alien and that somehow it was trying to say goodbye. "Bye then," he whispered as the little ship bobbed and hovered in front of him. "If you are a real alien and your ship really has been mended somehow, good luck and I hope you get home safely." In answer, the ship's lights flashed on and off and on and off and then it was gone, like a mini lightning streak, down the garden, over the apple tree and off into the sky.

The next morning Adam woke with a start and remembering his dream, he dived out of bed and ran to his chest of drawers where he had left his models and his drawing. It was very strange. His drawing was still there but had faded and become very faint almost drained of colour and energy, but what was even stranger was that there was no model spaceship or alien to be seen! Instead, next to the picture lay a different alien, the one that Adam had originally intended to buy! Adam was amazed. It was a lot to take in before breakfast but it seemed that he really had helped the alien to mend his broken ship! He had fixed the broken support in his mind, and put it on paper, and it had worked! Adam decided that it was all very strange but exciting! Before he could think about it properly though, he had to try and sneak Jones downstairs again, to avoid a telling off! After breakfast he decided, he would start his picture again and put all the colours back as best he could, and then he would hang it on his wall to remind him of last night's alien encounter. "Think we'll keep that little adventure to ourselves, don't you Jones?" he whispered to his dog as they crept downstairs. "What do you fancy for breakfast? I'm starving!" Adam smiled to himself as Jones gave a soft answering bark.

True ✔ or false ✗ ?

Decide which of these 20 statements are true or false. Check your answers on the next page – *but no cheating!*

1 The grizzly bear can run as fast as an average horse.

True ☐   False ☐

2 Salt was so valuable during Roman times that some soldiers were paid with it.

True ☐   False ☐

3 Glasgow is the capital of Scotland.

True ☐   False ☐

4 Sea hedgehogs, which are about one foot long, can kill sharks more than 20 feet long.

True ☐   False ☐

5 A boy who found a bar of 100-year-old frozen chocolate in a Swiss glacier was given a refund for it at a shop.

True ☐   False ☐

6 A parrot in Nottingham has been trained to pick up and answer its owner's telephone.

True ☐   False ☐

7 Some dinosaurs were as small as hens.

True ☐   False ☐

8 The blue whale can go for six months without eating.

True ☐   False ☐

9 Fleas can jump 160 times their own height.

True ☐   False ☐

10 Earthworms can climb trees to reach tasty fruit.

True ☐   False ☐

compiled by: Peter Barker and John Malam   illustrations: Mike Turner

11 An elephant is the only animal with four knees.

True ☐   False ☐

12 The well known Spider plant gets its name from tiny spiders that live on it.

True ☐   False ☐

13 When Eddie the Eagle produced the shortest ski jump in Olympic history in 1994, the Olympic flame went out.

True ☐   False ☐

14 Spiders spin their webs with silk 15 times finer than human hair.

True ☐   False ☐

15 The energy produced by some computer games is so strong it can boil an egg placed on top of the machine.

True ☐   False ☐

16 There are 27 letters in the alphabet.

True ☐   False ☐

17 There are 10 planets in the solar system.

True ☐   False ☐

18 Scientists have trained a monkey to make cups of tea for them.

True ☐   False ☐

19 Some snakes can swallow animals as big as an antelope in just one mouthful.

True ☐   False ☐

20 A schoolgirl from the USA blew a bubble with her bubble gum that measured 19.25 inches wide.

True ☐   False ☐

ANSWERS						
1 T	4 T	7 T	10 F	13 F	16 F	19 T
2 T	5 F	8 T	11 F	14 T	17 F	20 T
3 F	6 F	9 T	12 F	15 F	18 F	

27

Make a pond

If you are working towards your World Conservation activity badge you may like to try building your own garden pond as part of the badge requirements (with the permission of your Cub Scout Leader). Even if you are not working for the badge, this is still a fun activity and a more than worthwhile contribution to wildlife conservation.

1 Where to dig the pond
The first thing to do is to find a location. If you are lucky enough to have a garden of your own, then fine. If not, ask around and see if you can make one for a relative or neighbour in your area. Avoid shaded areas and keep away from trees as fallen leaves can become a nuisance.

2 How big to make the pond
Once you have a site, you will have to decide on what size (the larger the better!) and type of pond you want. Prefabricated fibreglass ponds are available from garden centres but these are restrictive in size and

are not half as much fun as designing and building your own – *so get out those shovels and dig a hole!* Obviously, the size, depth and shape is up to you, but it is important to keep one end of the pond shallow so that once the pond is finished you can place a ramp (made from wood or wire) at this end to allow any animals that may be unlucky enough to fall in the pond to escape. Also, if young children are likely to be around, remember you will need to erect some kind of child-proof fence around the pond.

LAY A HOSEPIPE ON THE GROUND TO OUTLINE THE BASIC SHAPE OF YOUR POND

DIG OUT THE POND, REMEMBERING TO MAKE DIFFERENT LEVELS FOR PLANTS AND PONDLIFE

STRETCH TH POND-LINER OVER THE PO USE STONES TO WEIGH IT

CROSS-SECTION, SHOWING DIFFERENT LEVELS

text: Mike Brennan   illustrations: Maggie Brand

3 Lining the pond

Waterproof lining for your pond can be obtained from your local garden centre. The garden centre will advise you what type of lining you require. You can use the following formulae to determine how much liner you need:

Depth of pond x 2 + length of pond = **A**
Depth of pond x 2 + width of pond = **B**
A x B = amount of liner required

Water is very heavy and there is always the risk of the water's weight tearing your lining. To help prevent this happening, line your hole with a few layers of old newspaper before laying down your liner. Once this is done, put your liner in place and secure it all around the edges with heavy rocks and stones.

4 Filling the pond – water, weeds and wildlife

Water: You can fill your pond with ordinary tap water, but it will help your pond to become colonised with wildlife more quickly if you can introduce some water from an already established pond.

Weeds: To begin colonisation, first introduce some oxygen-producing plants such as Elodea Densa which will keep the water healthy for wildlife. Again, your local garden centre will be able to advise you on the most suitable types of plants. Remember to thin the plants out as they grow, to avoid the formation of too much algae.

Wildlife: Do not introduce goldfish into your pond. Try to catch some sticklebacks locally, along with any other established pondlife you may come across. If you are lucky, frogs, toads or newts will eventually find their own way to your pond, along with snails and water-based insects.

FILLING WITH WATER

COVER THE EDGES WITH TURF AND PLANTS, TO HIDE THE LINER

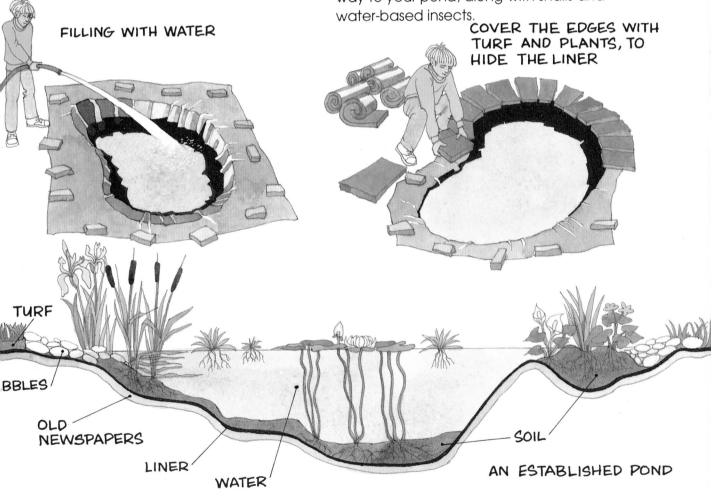

TURF

BBLES

OLD NEWSPAPERS

LINER

WATER

SOIL

AN ESTABLISHED POND

Be patient and in time you will find that you have created a pond world which not only plays an important part in conservation, but can also help you with parts of your Adventure Crest Award and your Naturalist and Scientist activity badges.

MAPS AND MAP-MAKING

A good map should give clear directions to help travellers find their way to places they may never have been to before. A map will also give travellers information about what they will see on their journey. If you wrote all of this information out in long-hand, such as "turn left at the crossroads, then go down the road for 200 metres, on your left is a large green house with a blue door, at this house turn right, on your left is a church with a tower...", the traveller would soon get lost if he tried to follow these directions. So let's take a look at how to make a map using symbols, and how the Ordnance Survey makes its detailed maps of the whole country.

A sketch map for a visitor

How do you give directions to a visitor who is coming to your house for the first time? You will need to know if your visitor is arriving in your town by road, rail, air or sea. If he is coming by road, draw the shapes of the main roads he should follow on to a piece of paper. If your visitor is coming by rail, air or sea, start by drawing the railway station, airport or harbour and then draw the roads leading to your house. Ideally, you should use graph paper to do this, but plain paper will do.

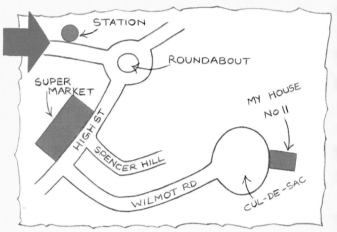

If your visitor is coming by car, your directions need to start further away from where you live. This is to help your visitor find his way to your town. One way to show this is by using the road numbers he should follow (such as A2022 or M6). Road numbers are often shown on major sign posts long before you see the name of the town the roads lead to. As your map gets nearer to your house, you should add the names of the roads your visitor should take (remember to mark on any one-way streets). Make sure that the names can be read easily.

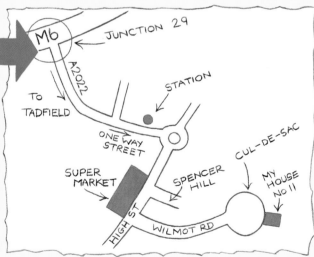

Mark landmarks on your map which will help your visitor pinpoint his position. You could mark roundabouts, shops, garages, traffic lights, parks, rivers, bridges, and so on. A map like this, is called a sketch map. It shows rough details which provide just enough information for the person who is to use the map.

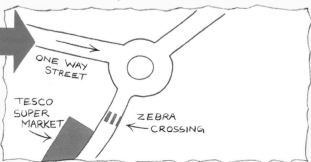

text: Ron Crabb   illustrations: Jane Pickering

Map out your house

Have a go at making a more detailed map than a sketch map. You could make a map of your house and garden, or if you live in a block of flats, the block and its surroundings, or maybe even a small section of your street.

First of all, make a rough drawing of the area to be mapped on white paper. Then measure out the most important distances by pacing them out (one fairly long stride measures about one metre). Next, transfer your sketch on to squared graph paper, but first, decide on a scale you will redraw it to – an ideal one is where one stride equals one square on the graph paper.

Using a ruler for any straight lines, draw in the house, any garages or sheds, paths, maybe a terrace, trees, pond or flower beds. You could use coloured pencils or crayons to brighten up your map. If you choose to do this, why not make a key for your map as well? A key will let people know what each of the colours stands for.

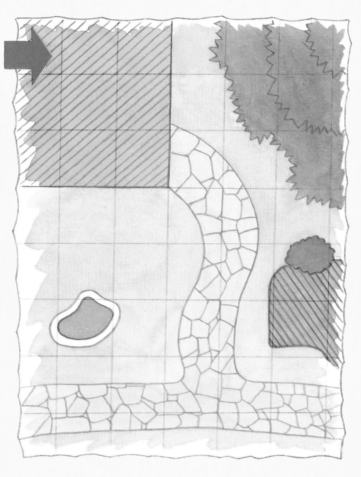

How do the professionals make maps?

Maps of the British Isles are drawn by the Ordnance Survey (often referred to simply as the OS). Since it was founded in 1791, the OS has earned itself a reputation as probably the best map-making organisation in the world. The original aim of the OS was to work out the position, using minute measurements and observations, of every man-made and natural feature of the land to a scale of one inch to one mile. This was a massive task which was completed using measuring chains, each made of 100 links.

Each metal chain measured 66 feet long and had to be laid down on the ground to make accurate measurements from object to object. You may think that this method sounds really old fashioned – however, it was in use right up until the 1950s!

Today, the OS carries out its map-making using much more sophisticated equipment than chains. A theodolite, which is like a telescope, allows the surveyors to make accurate measurements of angles and differences in heights between objects and places. Some theodolites use laser beams to guarantee pinpoint accuracy.

The OS also uses satellites to help with map-making, especially in areas where its surveyors cannot travel easily on foot, such as remote parts of the Scottish Highlands. Satellites can show differences in land heights, rock types and vegetation. They are so accurate that a map can be drawn without the surveyors having to step out of their office!

Make a game of blow football

You will need...
- ☆ A large cardboard box or lid
  The box must be a rectangle shape, at least 50cm long and 30cm wide.
  The base should be flat, with no joins.
- ☆ A plastic or foam cup
- ☆ Some sticky tape
- ☆ Non-toxic glue
- ☆ Green craft paper or green paint
- ☆ A thick felt-tip pen
- ☆ 2 drinking straws
- ☆ Some dried peas
- ☆ A pair of scissors
- ☆ A ruler

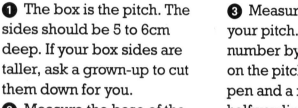

1 The box is the pitch. The sides should be 5 to 6cm deep. If your box sides are taller, ask a grown-up to cut them down for you.

2 Measure the base of the box. Cut out a piece of green craft paper the same size. Put a line of glue right round the edge of the craft paper on the **wrong** side. Press and smooth it down into the box base. You can paint the pitch green if you like, but let the paint dry before going on to step 3.

3 Measure the length of your pitch. Divide the number by 2. Mark this point on the pitch. Using a felt-tip pen and a ruler, draw in the halfway line.

4 Mark the middle of the halfway line. Draw around a jar or small saucer to mark the centre circle.

HALF-WAY POINT

GREEN CARD

GLUE

5 OR 6 CM DEEP

30CM

50CM

text: Brenda Apsley   illustrations: Jeannette Slater

⑤ Cut the plastic cup in half. Cut down one side, across the base and up the other side. Now you have 2 goals.

⑥ Tape a goal in place at each end of the pitch.

⑦ If you want to add some supporters, cut out lots of faces from comics and magazines. Glue them inside the sides of the pitch.

GAMES TO PLAY

Game 1
2 players
Each player needs a straw. Put 10 dried peas into the centre circle. Say "Kick off!" and try to blow the peas into your opponent's goal, while he tries to blow them into yours! You must not touch the balls with your straws. Move them around the pitch by blowing through your straws.

Game 2
4 or 6 players
Play the same game, but with 2 or 3 players on each team. The bigger your pitch, the more players can join in.

Game 3
As many players as you like
Play Game 1 like a knockout competition. The winners of the first round go on to round two, and so on, until you play a grand final.

Game 4
2 players
Play a game of football with one ball. Play for 3 minutes. Each time a goal is scored, put the ball back in the centre circle and kick off again. The winner is the player who has scored most goals at the end of the match. If the match ends in a draw, play 30 seconds of extra time.

Game 5
1 player
Test your shooting skills in a penalty shoot-out game. Line up 5 balls on the halfway line in the centre circle. You are allowed just one blow for each ball. How many goals can you score?

Feed Me!

If the subject of plants makes you yawn, prepare to be woken up. Because if you attempt to grow any of the plants we are about to find out about here, you will constantly be counting your fingers – these hungry plants are carnivorous!

The Venus Fly Trap (DIONAEA MUSCIPULA)

A native of Carolina in the USA, this is probably the most famous of all the carnivorous plants, although it is very rare in the wild.

The leaves of the Venus Fly Trap are narrow at one end but then expand into two large pads. Along the edge of the pads are soft spines. When an insect lands or crawls on to a pad the trap snaps shut. The spines act like prison bars, preventing the insect from escaping. The leaves then press together whilst secreting a liquid into the trap which digests the unfortunate victim.

The Dracula Plant
(SARRACENIA FLAVA)

Also known as the Tender Trap or the Yellow Trumpet, this plant is a native of North America.

In summer the plant produces a sticky sweet liquid at the top of its tubular leaf which attracts insects. As an insect walks into the tube it is tempted by more sweet food as it goes further down. When it tries to crawl back out of the tube after feasting on the sweet liquid, the insect is prevented from doing so by hairs which point downward. Even flying out is restricted by a 'roof' which hangs over the trap. The sweet liquid also makes the insect dizzy. Eventually, it falls back and is trapped. As with the Venus Fly Trap, the victim is dissolved by digestive juices which then feed the plant.

▲ Above: *a big meal for a Venus fly trap as it eats a young frog.*

◄ Left: a *tempting tube – but there's no way out for curious insects that venture inside the Dracula Plant.*

text: Mike Brennan

Oxford Scientific Films/Jack Dermid

The Cobra Lily (DARLINGTONIA CALIFORNICA)

This pitcher plant is closely related to the Dracula Plant and is also a native of North America. It is named after its similarity in appearance to a cobra snake about to strike.

Insects, usually flies, enter the trap through a hole underneath the 'roof' of the pitcher. Once inside they find it difficult to find the hole to get out again. The victim eventually becomes exhausted trying to escape. It falls to the bottom of the trap where strong digestive juices eat it away.

The Sundew (DROSERA ROTUNDIFOLIA)

The round-leaved Sundew is quite common in Britain and can be found in bog areas and on wet heaths.

The Sundew has flat, circular green leaves which are covered in red hairs. On the end of each hair is a tiny drop of sticky liquid. The liquid looks like dew, has a sugary taste and attracts insects. As an insect tries to feed on the liquid it sticks to the leaf and begins to struggle. The struggling movement causes the whole leaf to slowly bend over, sandwiching the insect between two layers of leaf. Digestive fluids do the rest!

Oxford Scientific Films/Zig

Oxford Scientific Films/James H Robinson

◀ Above left: *what insects are on the menu for these Cobra Lilies?*
▲ Above right: *drops of sticky liquid glisten on Sundew leaves – a super-glue to hold insect victims.*

Grow your own Venus Fly Trap

You might be able to buy a Venus Fly Trap from your local garden centre.

Here are some useful tips on how to look after it:

- ▲ Stand the pot in a saucer containing rainwater or distilled water.
- ▲ Never use tap water.
- ▲ Keep the plant in a warm, bright place.
- ▲ Cut off any flower stalks as soon as they appear.
- ▲ If you repot it, plant it in a mixture of two parts peat-free growing mixture and one part sand.

Oxford Scientific Films/Sean Morris

Be a Puppeteer

There are lots of famous puppets that you see on television and at the theatre. Before we show you how to make a few simple puppets of your own, see if you can fill in the missing words that are linked with famous puppets…
the answers are at the bottom of the next page.

Zig and _ _ _ _
Orville the _ _ _ _ _
Miss _ _ _ _ _ and _ _ _ _ _ _ the frog
Nookie _ _ _ _
Scorch the D _ _ _ _ _
_ _ _ _ _ _ _ Scarlet
Parker and Lady _ _ _ _ _ _ _ _ _

FIST FACES

Make your hand into a fist and move your thumb so that the tip of it is touching the knuckle of your index finger (the one next to the thumb). See if you can move your thumb up and down but keeping the tip of it touching the knuckle. This will be the mouth of your puppet.

Now draw two eyes with a felt pen or face paints and you have your instant puppet! You could make a hat from paper, hair using wool and even add funny teeth.

KNEE FACES

Put on a pair of shorts and stand up. Flex the muscles in one knee and see if your knee cap moves about (not everyone can do this!). If it does, you can use a felt pen or face paints to draw a funny face on your knee. When you flex your muscles this time, the face will move around as though it is talking.

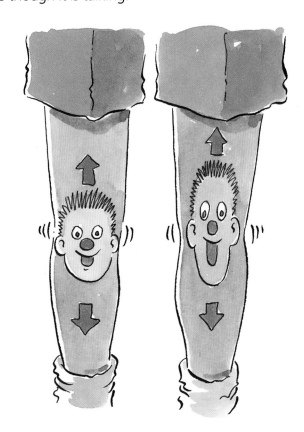

text: Emma Wood   illustrations: Ann Johns

FINGER FOLK

Trace around the outline shown here and colour it in – you could make it your favourite footballer or film star. Use sticky tape or an elastic band to stick it to the two fingers closest to your thumb. These two fingers will be your puppet's legs and feet.

Your puppet is now ready for action. Your friend could make one too and you could set up a table-top soccer match between your two finger folk, using a ping-pong ball or marble as a football.

KAA THE SNAKE

Make your very own Kaa the Snake, from *The Jungle Book*, using an old long sock, an elastic band, some wool and some sticky paper.

Put the sock on your hand so that the heel of the sock is on the top side of your wrist as shown here. Then, put the elastic band around your four fingers, pushing it as far into the V between the thumb and the index finger as it will go. Your thumb is the bottom jaw of the snake, the fingers are the top – practise opening and closing the mouth. On some white sticky labels, draw two big round eyes. Cut them out and stick them on the top of your hand.

If you want to really surprise people with your snake, find a shoebox, cut a hole in one end that your arm can fit through, put lots of torn-up paper in it and close the lid. Hold the box with your other arm and ask a friend to lift the lid – your snake can suddenly come alive and scare them!

37

Shadow the REPORTER

It was nearing half-term holiday and Patrick and Luke, two Cub Scouts who were really good friends, were wondering what they could do during the holidays. So when their Akela challenged each Cub to complete an Activity Badge during the half-term holiday, Patrick and Luke had an idea.

Patrick was a Sixer and he found out that Luke had always wanted to gain his Communicator badge, so Patrick planned a way of helping Luke. Patrick told his Akela what Luke wanted to do. Their Akela arranged for them to visit their local newspaper offices to find out how a newspaper reporter works. David Bryant was one of the reporters on the *Surrey Comet* newspaper, based in Twickenham, and he explained his job to Patrick and Luke.

❶ *David showed Patrick and Luke something from the previous week's issue. It was an article he had written, and they could see it on the computer screen and also printed in the newspaper.*

❷ *"Hello, 'Surrey Comet'. How can I help you?" A new story was coming in for David. Patrick and Luke watched him make some notes. He would use the notes to help him write the story later.*

Writing the story

David writes his 'copy' at a desk in the office ('copy' is the name given to a story or feature). He covers the Twickenham area and he explained how he found out about news stories. *"Mainly from something called a Press Release,"* said David, *"which is a letter someone sends to us with lots of clear facts and information about something that is going to happen. So, if you have any news, send your local newspaper a Press Release. Sometimes I have to interview someone or speak to them on the telephone. When I do an interview I have a notepad with me and make notes as the person speaks. My job is to take the facts from a Press Release or an interview and turn them into a story that people will want to read in the newspaper. If they don't read it, we won't sell newspapers and I could be out of a job!"*

Typing up the story

David uses a special computer which lets him type his copy for a news story on to the screen. He can then make it longer or shorter and make sure that it is interesting for people to read – this is called editing. His computer screen tells him exactly the width his copy will be when it goes on to the printed page and how many lines and columns it will take up as well. It also has a spelling checker – very useful when you have a lot to type up!

When David has finished typing up a story, he shows it to the Chief Reporter. The Chief Reporter's job is to look at the work of all of the news reporters to make sure they are working properly, and that what they have written can actually be printed. Sometimes it can't be printed, because someone may take offence to it. But most of the time the copy is good and it is cleared to go to the Editor.

The Editor

The Editor sees all the copy for the newspaper, including reports about sport, television, theatre and other local events. The Editor looks at everything and decides what is to go into the newspaper and where it will go.

❶

❷

text and photographs: Ron Crabb

3 David explained that newspaper stories have to fit into carefully measured spaces. If there were too many words he would have to take some out. If there were not enough words, he would have to write some more. He used the computer behind him to write his stories.

4 "A local newspaper should provide a service for people who read it. They should be able to get all sorts of information from it," said David. "Like the football fixtures?" asked Luke. "Yes – and the results," added David.

5 An interview in progress – the Cubs ask the questions and David makes the notes.

When the Editor has checked the copy, it is transmitted by telephone to a team of designers using a device called a 'modem'. The designers position the copy and any photographs on to pages, according to where the Editor has said they should go. The designers then send a sample copy (called a 'proof') to the Editor for one final check. If it's all OK, the newspaper can then be printed.

Doing an interview

The *Surrey Comet* had recently changed its shape from being a large-sized paper (called a 'broadsheet', like *The Times* or *The Independent*) to being a smaller-sized paper (called a 'tabloid', like *The Sun* or *Daily Mail*). What did people think about this change? Luke wanted to find out for himself, and David said he should ask some questions and actually do an interview. David invited Luke and Patrick to have a go at interviewing someone. They left the *Surrey Comet* offices and stopped a passer-by in the street to ask him some questions.

"*What do you think of the new-look 'Surrey Comet'?*" asked Luke.

"*It looks brilliant,*" said the passer-by, "*and good value for money.*" David scribbled in his notepad as the man spoke.

When they had finished interviewing the man, they went back inside and typed up some copy for the next edition of the newspaper. They called their story *What do you think?*

"*Well? What did you think of that?*" Patrick asked Luke.

"*I want to be a reporter one day,*" Luke replied, as they made their way back to Patrick's home. All the way, Luke was thinking...*I wonder what badge Patrick wants to do?*

How our badges are made

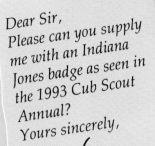

*T*his was the letter we received from Cub Scout, Alex Spaven of the 11th Weston Favell Cub Scout Pack in Northampton. What were we to do? There is no such badge as an Indiana Jones badge in the Cub Scout programme and, to produce just one, would cost thousands of pounds.

> Dear Sir,
> Please can you supply me with an Indiana Jones badge as seen in the 1993 Cub Scout Annual?
> Yours sincerely,
>
> *Alex Spaven*
> Alex Spaven

Above: *Alex Spaven outside the Coventry factory of J & J Cash, with his guide for the day, Tony Archer.*

Below: *Alex watches as a badge designer uses a computer to design the 1995 World Jamboree badge.*

Over to Scout Shops Limited

Scout Shops Limited are the people who supply our badges for all in the Scout Movement. Ian Chalmers, the Company Secretary of Scout Shops Limited, came to the rescue when he arranged for Alex and his mum to visit the factory of J & J Cash Limited of Coventry. Cash's makes many of the badges that Beaver Scouts, Cub Scouts, Scouts and Venture Scouts wear on their uniforms, so who better to show Alex how a badge is made? With his 16 Activity badges proudly displayed on his uniform, Alex brought many of the badges full circle – back to where they were made!

Noisy, clanking looms

Some of you may know about, or even have, the kits you can buy to enable you to paint-by-numbers. It is a system like this that Cash's used to use to make badges. Making badges using this system took a long time and, from there, the design had to be transferred to very noisy weaving looms. If you can think of 300 massive mechanical looms in one room all clanking and chugging away at the same time, you can imagine that it would be virtually impossible to hear someone speak or shout to you. These days, the whole operation is computerised which means making badges is very much quieter and quicker.

The World Membership badge on a weaving loom. You can see how the badge is woven in long, thin strips which are then cut up into individual badges.

text and photographs: David Easton

40

From the design...

Alex was lucky to see the first designs of the 1995 World Jamboree badge being worked on by a designer on his computer. Alex enjoyed this as he, too, is 'into' computers, and it was difficult to tear him away from that first stage. Then he went to the main design studio and saw designs for some of the other products made by Cash's, such as woven bookmarks and greetings cards. You may have seen some of these in the shops.

... to the weaving room

Inside the badge weaving room, Alex saw huge looms stretching as far as his eyes could see. Each loom was weaving together many multi-coloured threads, producing row upon row of badges which rolled off the end of the looms in great, continuous sheets. The looms follow a computer pattern drawn by the badge designer.

Alex saw clothes labels for well known shops being produced by what seemed to be the million. He saw souvenir badges for football clubs being made and cut to shape, and was given some to take home! He saw name tapes, luggage straps and supermarket trolley straps being produced in long strips, and all carefully checked for quality.

Alex is shown the working part of a weaving loom.

One of the bonuses of the day was to see the 1994 Unite project badges being edged and overlocked.

The Unite badge was worn by everyone in the Scout Movement during 1994. Each badge was woven in three colours and contained 837 individual stitches! The Unite badge was the result of a project between The Scout Association and UNICEF (the United Nations International Children's Emergency Fund). The badge showed the colours of the flag of Uganda and a bird known as the Balearic Crested Crane.

HOW DOES A CUB SCOUT 1995 POSTCODE WORK?

This was a question asked by four very inquisitive Cub Scouts: Martin, Matthew, Lasanka and Jo, who were all working towards their Writers badge at Cubs. To find out how a postcode really works, they visited Nine Elms sorting office, in London – the second largest sorting office in the capital. It sorts almost two million parcels and envelopes every week and sends them out to local post offices for distribution.

A Coding Operator, Tony Shackell, was there to help and he took the four Cubs all the way through the process of the job of Nine Elms.

The first stop was the Arrival Room, where all the mail comes to from local post offices and different businesses. When it arrives at Nine Elms, first class post is in grey bags, second class post in red bags and overseas post in green bags – this makes it easier for sorting into areas and types of post. But some people in businesses put letters in the wrong coloured bags and the post sorters at Nine Elms have to check through it all.

The post bags are emptied into large containers. These containers are called 'jumbos' and each one has a bottom shaped like a concertina. The jumbos are wheeled over to a large conveyor belt where they are emptied out. The letters and parcels are then roughly hand checked to make sure they are all first or second class. Then they are bagged up again and sent along to a massive sorting machine that's like a tumble dryer. This is the Culler Facer Canceller machine, or CFC for short. At this stage, any parcels, or really large envelopes, are placed on to a massive conveyor belt which stretches all the way around the ceiling of the building to an exit.

The CFC machine is huge and can sort up to 26,000 letters and small packets every hour when it really gets going. It works by spinning all of the letters and parcels around in its drum and they slide in between slots in the walls of the drum, depending on their size. The larger parcels are tipped out at the other end of the drum and go on a conveyor belt to another part of the sorting office. The Cubs couldn't miss the opportunity to have a go at loading the CFC and gave a helping hand to its operators by emptying the mail bags into the machine.

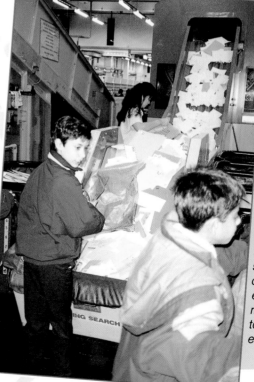

❶ The Cubs helped to empty one of the grey bags from a 'jumbo' on to the conveyor belt that fed the CFC machine.

❷ Letters are emptied on to a conveyor belt that leads up to the CFC machine. Inside the machine is a large drum which spins round and round, sorting the mail into different-sized envelopes. The machine can sort up to 26,000 letters every hour!

text and photographs: Ron Crabb

Some letters slip through the CFC and these then go through another machine which takes them around a series of belts. They go off to other parts of Nine Elms sorting office to be checked. One such place is the postcode area, which is where Tony works.

Tony showed the Cubs how the postcode machine works. If people are not sure what the postcode is of the place they are sending their letter to, the letter goes to Tony and he has to look it up and key a code into his machine. In front of him he has a short list of postcodes and if it isn't on his list, he may know it himself. But if he doesn't, he has to pass it on and someone else may know. If, after every one of the coding operators has seen it, they still don't know the postcode, someone has to look it up in a big book. A similar operation is done with the parcels.

Tony's machine prints small blue dots on the front of the envelopes. The blue dots contain phosphor which can be read by a machine called a Philtec Reader. The blue dots represent a particular postcode. The Philtec Reader has within it a 'magic eye' which can look at the envelope, look at the phosphor dots and work out where it should be going. It then sends it along to a special box just for that place and leaves it there for one of the sorters to come and collect every so often.

The Nine Elms sorting office was just fitting in a new machine which doesn't even need the blue phosphor dots and can just read the address from the envelope, but people like Tony will still be needed when people forget to write a postcode on their envelopes. Once this machine is running, people will really need to make sure that their postcode is clearly written, so that the machine can read it properly.

When all of the letters and parcels have been sorted for one area, they are placed into large mail sacks and sent out to the postal town using lorries. There they are taken to the local post office and sorted for the individual postmen to deliver on their rounds.

The Cubs saw how much faster the post is delivered if people use postcodes. If they don't, it causes extra work for people like Tony – and that means the post takes longer to reach its destination. With their new found knowledge, the Cubs went back to their Pack and told all of the other Cubs just how important it is to write an address properly. They all gained their Writers badge.

3 Tony sat at his postcode machine and showed the Cubs how to tap a postcode in.

4 Small blue dots containing phosphor are stamped on to envelopes at this machine. The dots represent the postcode and can be 'read' by other machines in the sorting office. Look out for the blue dots on your post at home!

5 Lasanka helped to sort some of the mail by hand.

HOW DOES A CUB SCOUT 1995 POSTCODE WORK?

Bird feeders to make

Birds have a hard life in winter. There is not much food around, and they need to eat to keep warm. You can help feed birds by making your own bird feeders out of objects you might have at home.

Peanut bottle bird feeder

You will need…
- ★ An empty washing-up liquid bottle
- ★ 1m length of string
- ★ A 20cm piece of thin wooden dowelling

This is what you do…

❶ Wash the empty bottle and top very carefully. Rinse and dry.

❷ Mark 2 lines down the bottle, one on each side. Start at the top and stop 5cm from the bottom.

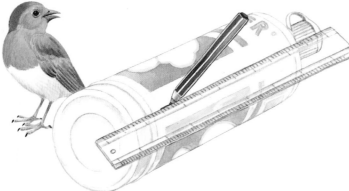

❸ Cut around the lines to make 2 narrow slits 7 to 8mm wide. The slits should be wide enough for beaks to get in, but not so wide that peanuts fall out! Ask a grown-up to help you.

❹ Snip the stopper off the top. Thread both ends of the string through the top. Knot the ends together inside. This makes a hanging loop.

❺ Make a hole under each slit, 3cm from the base. Push the wooden dowelling through the holes to make 2 perches for the birds to sit on. If you cannot find dowelling, use a pencil instead.

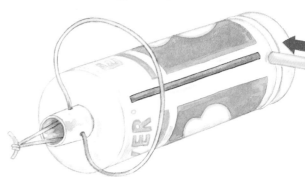

❻ Fill the bottle with **unsalted** peanuts, or mix the peanuts with tiny cubes of bread and cheese. Put the top on, and hang outside from a tree or nail. Make sure cats cannot catch the birds as they feed.

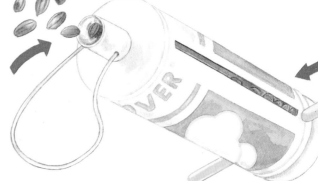

★ A helpful hint ★
You could use a waxed paper milk carton in the same way, but it will not last as long as the plastic bottle.

text: Brenda Apsley   illustrations: Jane Pickering

Mixed food egg box bird feeder

You will need…
★ An egg box base, plastic **not** cardboard
★ 1m length of string

This is what you do…
❶ Make a hole at each corner of the egg box base.
❷ Cut the string into 4 x 25cm pieces. Tie a knot at the end of each piece.

❸ Push a piece of string **up** through each hole. Knot all 4 ends together to make a hanging loop.
❹ Fill each egg hole with different foods: sunflower seeds, tiny cubes of bread, **unsalted** peanuts, leftover cooked potatoes, apple cores. Fill the last egg with water. Hang from a branch or hook.

★A helpful hint ★
In very cold weather, add a little warm water to the water section to stop it freezing. Many birds die of thirst in winter. Feed the birds regularly. They will get used to visiting you, and will come to rely on your help.
Don't forget birds that like to feed on the ground, such as thrushes. Put out a saucer of water for them, and scatter some food on the ground under the feeder.

CAN YOU?

Here's a great selection of challenges for you to try on your own, or for you to challenge a friend to do. They might look easy, but are really quite hard to do!

text: Emma Wood   illustrations: Ann Johns

1 BLINDFOLD BALANCE

Stand on one leg, with the other leg raised well off the ground. It's quite easy to balance like this, isn't it?

Can You…

Shut your eyes tightly and keep them closed for one minute. I bet you can't stand upright without moving your feet around for the whole minute!

2 EGG SPINNING

Take an unboiled hen's egg, lay it on its side on a table top and spin it round. Easy, isn't it?

Can You…

Now, try and spin it on one of its ends. I bet you won't be able to do it! (But you can do it if you use a hard-boiled egg. Maybe you could challenge a friend to do this – he uses a raw egg and, unknown to him, you use a hard-boiled one!)

3 PAPER FOLDING

Take a sheet of paper and fold it in half. Now fold it in half again…and then again.

Can You…

I bet you can't fold it more than seven times like this. Try using big sheets of paper, or really thin paper… can you fold it more than seven times?

4 LISTEN CAREFULLY

Say to a friend the following: "Put two chairs together, side-by-side, stand behind the chairs with your feet together, take off your shoes and then jump over them."

Can You…

Your friend will try to jump over the chairs (feet must be kept together – no run-ups allowed). All he really needed to do was jump over his shoes, not the chairs – but I bet he didn't listen to your instructions properly!

5 BICYCLE BALANCE

Find a soft patch of grass in a park or garden and sit on a bicycle. Pedal forwards as slowly as you can – it's quite easy, isn't it?

Can You...
Stop the bicycle and cross your hands so that you are holding the handlebars with different hands. Now try and pedal slowly forwards – I bet you can't even move half a metre without toppling over!

6 HEADS 'N' HANDS

Take your right hand and pat yourself gently on the top of your head. Easy! Relax and then try rubbing the palm of your left hand in a circular pattern on your tummy. Even easier!

Can You...
Do both of these actions at the same time? I bet you can't!

7 FACE GRABBING

Lightly hold your nose with the fingers on your right hand and, at the same time, hold your right ear with your left hand.

Can You...
Slap your thighs with both hands at the same time and quickly hold your nose with your left hand and hold your left ear with your right hand.

Keep doing this, swapping hands and slapping your thighs to build up a rhythm. Do this with a friend, keeping time with each other – see who makes a mistake first and holds the wrong ear with the wrong hand!

8 ALPHABET SCRAMBLE

Challenge a friend to say the alphabet backwards. However hard he tries, I bet he can't do it.

Can You...
When he gives up, all you need do is to say the words 'The Alphabet Backwards', and you will have done it!

Cub Castle

Jonathan Simpson of the 54th Bury (Brandlesholme Methodist) Cub Scout Pack has made a super castle...with just a little help from some grown-ups. By following these step-by-step instructions, you too can make your very own Cub Castle.

You will need:

- 5 sheets of thick cartridge or craft paper, each about 60cm square
- 4 tall cardboard tubes (from kitchen rolls)
- 4 wooden cocktail sticks
- Sticky tape and non-toxic craft glue
- Scissors and a sharp craft knife
- Pencil and ruler
- Poster paints, felt-tip pens and paintbrushes

Castle walls – side walls

There are 3 identical side walls to make. You may need to ask a grown-up for some help.

1 For each side wall use 1 of the pieces of thick paper. Draw the wall on to the paper, following the diagram. Follow the measurements as closely as you can.

3 Use the craft knife to cut out the battlements. Be careful not to cut in the wrong place – only cut along complete lines, not along dashed lines (these are fold lines).

4 Lightly score along the fold lines.

5 Fold the castle wall along each fold line. Use sticky tape or glue to hold the pieces together.

15mm

20mm

20mm (FLAP)

170mm

20mm

70mm

170mm

180mm

2 Cut the wall out. Cut neatly and in straight lines.

6 Repeat steps 1 to 5 until you have built the 3 side walls.

text: Brenda Apsley   model: Wayne Pretl & Jeannette Slater   illustrations: Jeannette Slater

Castle wall – drawbridge wall

1 Draw the drawbridge wall on to the paper, following this diagram:

2 Repeat steps 2 to 5 of the side wall instructions, remembering to cut along the drawbridge lines. One piece of the drawbridge folds out from the wall, the other piece folds and tucks inside the wall (look at the photo to see how this works).

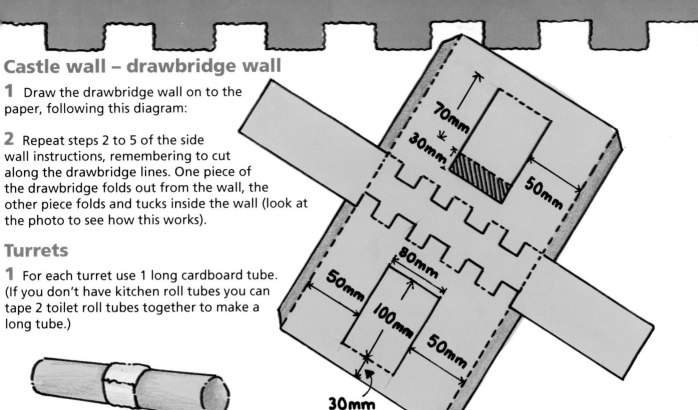

Turrets

1 For each turret use 1 long cardboard tube. (If you don't have kitchen roll tubes you can tape 2 toilet roll tubes together to make a long tube.)

2 Make the 4 turret roofs. Cut them out of the thick paper, following the diagram. Mark where the centre point is (this will help you with step 3).

3 Bend each roof into a cone shape and tape the edges together on the inside.

4 Make 4 turret flags. For each one, draw and cut out a card flag, like the one below.

5 Push a cocktail stick through each flag. Then push the flags through the tops of the turret roofs.

6 Put some glue on the top edge of each turret and press the roof in place. Leave to dry.

Painting the castle
Paint the turrets and walls with poster paint, or artist's gouache paint if you have some. Use lots of imagination! Don't forget to paint the inside of the castle. Add details like windows and arrow slits using a black felt-tip pen. Leave the pieces to dry before you join them all together.

Assembling the castle
Put Cub Castle together. Tape and glue the 4 walls with a turret at each corner. If you like, add a base. Paint a large, flat piece of cardboard grey for the castle floor and green outside, like grass. You could even paint a moat of blue water – but make sure the drawbridge will stretch over it! Use some flat pieces of card to make trees and bushes.

Good tips...
■ You can make a simpler type of castle by using cut-down cereal boxes. You could use the pointed parts of an egg tray to make the battlements. If you cover the boxes with craft paper, you can colour the castle, like the one in our photo.
■ If you have some Lego figures, use them to guard the castle and patrol its walls.

Build your own VOLCANO

Have you ever seen pictures of a volcano erupting? Volcanoes are a bit like a valve on the top of a pressure cooker or on a steam train's boiler. When the lid of a pressure cooker is put on and you start to cook, steam builds up inside the pan. The valve on the top of the lid lets some of the steam escape before the pressure inside the pan gets too great. If there was no valve, the pan might explode!

A volcano is a pressure valve for the Earth. In the middle of the planet is a core of molten rock. It is so hot that it would cook a baked potato in one second! Like in the pressure cooker, steam and gases build up and they need somewhere to escape. These gases, steam and even some of the molten rock (called lava) rise to the surface of the planet and escape through holes in the ground called volcanoes.

Millions of years ago, when the world was being formed, there were volcanoes everywhere – including Great Britain. Today, there are still active volcanoes in some parts of the world, especially in parts of southern Europe, the Far East and the American continents. Some volcanoes, such as the ones on Iceland, are constantly erupting.

You can build your very own working volcano by following the instructions below – but don't worry, your volcano won't have any hot steam or molten lava coming from it!

You will need...

★ An empty camera film canister
★ Modelling clay or plaster of Paris
★ Bicarbonate of soda (you can buy this from any supermarket)
★ Vinegar

This is what you do...

1. Remove the lid from the film canister.
2. Place the empty canister on a piece of cardboard.

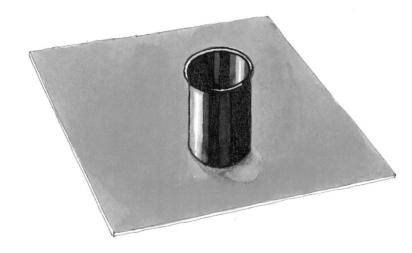

text: Emma Wood   illustrations: Maggie Brand

Some famous volcanic eruptions of the past

Volcano name	Country	Date	What happened?
Santorini	Greek island	1550BC	Almost destroyed the island and probably led to the destruction of the Minoan civilisation.
Vesuvius	Italy	AD79	Destroyed the Roman towns of Pompeii, Herculanium and Stabiae.
Etna	Sicily, Italy	1669	20,000 people died in a massive eruption.
Krakatoa	Indonesia	1883	The greatest volcanic explosion recorded. Over 36,000 people died and the sound of the eruption was heard over one thirteenth of the Earth's surface.
Mont Pelée	West Indies	1902	The town of St Pierre was destroyed, killing all its people – except for one prisoner who survived inside the town's strong prison!
Mount St Helens	USA	1980	A vast area of forest was destroyed, a river changed its course and a volcanic ash was blown up to 800 kilometres away.
Mount Pinatubo	Philippines	1991/2	A mud flow buried several hundred villages, destroyed crops and livestock and drove away tens of thousands of people. It will take 50 years for the mud to settle. This was the first eruption of the volcano for more than 600 years.

3 Use the clay or plaster of Paris to build a volcano shape around the canister, being sure to leave a small hole at the top to act as the crater. The hole should be smaller than the mouth of the canister.

4 You are now ready for action! Drop two spoonfuls of the bicarbonate of soda into the crater, followed by two spoonfuls of vinegar. Your volcano should start to bubble and froth up and your 'lava' will slowly erupt out of the volcano and down its sides.

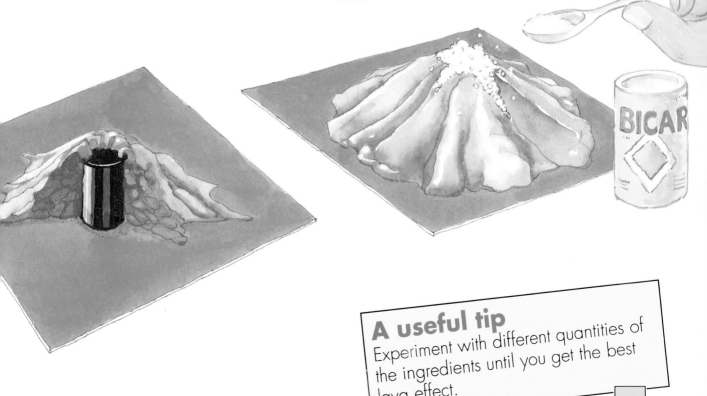

A useful tip
Experiment with different quantities of the ingredients until you get the best lava effect.

Tracking signs and tracking

At the beginning of this century, there lived a very famous soldier called Robert Baden-Powell. Robert was clever and he wrote many books, drew hundreds of pictures and met thousands of people.

When he left the army, he created the Scout Movement and spent all his time teaching people about Scouting. He was good at most things but there was one activity in particular in which he was very skilful – tracking. Robert could follow animals and people with great ease and was an expert at laying detailed trails to guide people through unknown areas.

Even today, people still 'track' animals and special signs are used by people to show others which way they have gone, or to help them find their way back over a difficult part of a route or journey.

Here are some of the special signs that have been designed over the years to help people lay trails and enable others to 'track' them down. All the signs use natural materials such as twigs and stones. This is so that people can lay trails that will not look out of place and will only be recognised by those people who know what they are looking for.

'I've gone straight on' signs

'Do not go this way' signs

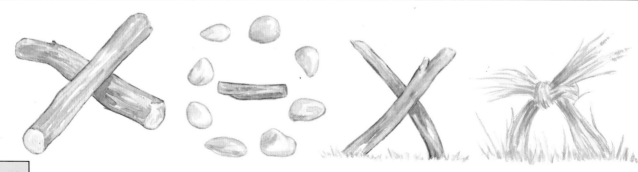

text: Peter Barker   illustrations: Jane Pickering

'I've turned left' or 'I've turned right' signs

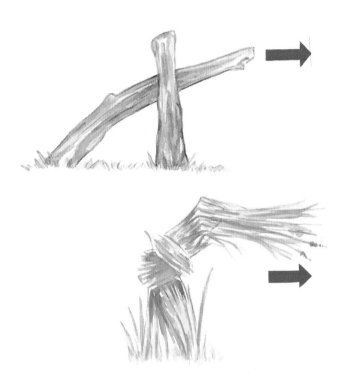

'I've left a message close to the trail' sign
(This sign could give more detailed instructions about where you have gone.)

'I've gone home' sign
(Use this sign at the end of your trail to let your trackers know you have finished and gone home.)

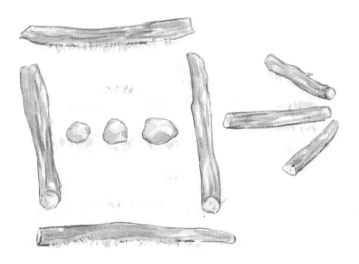

Try using some of these signs to lay a trail for your friends to follow. When you have practised using these, why not design your own tracking signs that only you and your friends will recognise?

The game of soccer has come a long way since 1863, when the Football Association was formed to set up an official set of rules for the sport. Today, soccer is a popular sport in almost every country in the world. Little wonder, then, that it has produced some rather unusual 'results'.

It's a funny old game

A game of several halves

During the third round of the FA Cup in 1955, Stoke City and Bury met a total of five times, drawing on four occasions, before Stoke finally clinched the match by winning 3–2. The games amounted to 9 hours and 22 minutes of play!

Mind your head

On 3 January 1977, Torquay United's Pat Kruse equalled the record for the fastest goal on record by scoring only 6 seconds after the kick-off. The only problem was he headed the ball into his own net, much to the delight of opponents Cambridge!

A pack of red cards

In June 1993 it was reported that a league match between Sportivo Ameliano and General Caballero of Paraguay had to be abandoned because so many of the players had been sent off. Originally, two Sportivo players were sent off the pitch, sparking off a ten minute fight between the teams. The referee then sent off a further 18 players – including the entire Sportivo team!

text: Mike Brennan   illustrations: Andy Robb

54

Cheats sometimes prosper

In order to gain promotion in 1979, the Yugoslavian team Ilinden FC needed to improve their goal difference by the end of the season. With the help of the referee and their opponents, Mladost, Ilinden managed to win their final game of the season 134–1. Their rivals in the championship hatched a similar plot but only managed to win their final game 88–0.

Give it to the goalie

Goalkeepers come in all shapes and sizes but by far the biggest in professional football was England international Willie Henry 'Fatty' Foulke (1874–1916). Weighing in at a hefty 141kg (22st) and standing to a height of 1.90m (6ft 3in), Willie once stopped a game by accidentally snapping the cross bar. He played his last games for Bradford City by which time his weight had increased to a mighty 165kg (26st).

To pay or not to pay?

The smallest paying attendance at an English Football League game was for the Stockport County v Leicester City match at Old Trafford, Manchester, in May 1921. Only 13 people paid to see the game, although it is estimated that around 2,000 supporters managed to gain 'free' admission!

You'll never walk alone...

The greatest recorded crowd for any football match was 199,589 for a World Cup tie between Brazil and Uruguay at Maracana Municipal Stadium in 1950.

You could hear a pin drop

Due to disciplinary action by the European Football Union, West Ham played to an empty Upton Park in 1980 against Castilla of Spain. In 1982 Aston Villa played to an empty Villa Park, against Besiktas of Turkey.

Inside the world of the

GLADIATORS ™

In October 1992, the most exciting new concept in sports entertainment hit the UK's television screens when 'Gladiators' appeared in over 13 million homes across the country. The programme became an instant success and is now in its third series. But how was the world of the Gladiators created? Here we go behind the scenes to find out...

Mini models

The first stage involved making detailed models in miniature. Designers, illustrators and model makers made scale models in plastic. Every game was worked out in fine detail, right down to the ridges, bumps and cracks in 'The Wall' – one of the show's challenging games.

Turning the models into reality

The set took 75 people two months to make. A firm of specialist scenery makers turned the designers' ideas into life-size versions of the models. Twenty-five miles of electric cables were used and almost 1,000 lamps were hoisted to their correct positions high up above the floor of the Arena. Safety experts tested every single piece of equipment. Nothing was left unchecked. For 'The Wall', mountaineering experts were called in to thoroughly test it before the Gladiators and contenders were allowed on to it. The safety ropes used on 'The Wall' are tough enough to hold a one tonne weight!

Fourteen super-fit men and women whose skill, speed and stamina earns them the honour of being the Gladiators.

Gladiators' is filmed at the National Indoor Arena, in Birmingham. Each time a new series is filmed there, it takes at least three to five days to transform this national sports stadium into the high-tech world of the Gladiators. When filming is over, the games and the set are dismantled and stored away, ready for the next time they are needed.

Enter the Gladiators

The Gladiators are super-fit men and women, specially chosen for their strength and stamina. To keep 'in shape', each Gladiator undergoes a strict training and diet programme. On an actual show day, the Gladiators between them eat their way through 28 chicken breasts, 18 pounds of turkey, 12 pounds of salmon, 16 steaks, 46 jacket potatoes, 24 eggs and 22 yoghurts – and that's before they've started on the contenders!

Enter the contenders

Thousands of sportsmen and women from all over Britain have tried to become contenders, but only a handful have reached the ultimate challenge – to enter the Gladiators' Arena. If you can run 800 metres in 2½ minutes, do 10 hanging chin-ups, traverse a horizontal ladder and then climb a 30ft. rope (twice!), then you're well on the way to becoming a contender. But, if all this exercise proves too much, then you'll just have to stay on the touchline and watch the event from a safe distance – along with millions of other fans!

Top: 'The Wall' is one of the toughest games on 'Gladiators' – a 36-feet-high challenge.
Above: Over you go! A brave contender feels the strength of his Gladiator opponent in 'The Duel'.
Left: 'Tilt' is like a tug of war, but played way above the ground.

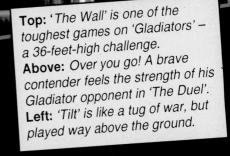

Note: Gladiators and contenders have undergone considerable training – do not attempt to imitate their actions or recreate Gladiator events. PLAY SAFELY.

ALEX KIDD

SEGA PRIZE

3 SEGA Master Systems to be won!

The Sega Master System II is one of the most popular video game units around and comes complete with everything you need for instant game action. You don't even need a game cartridge to start with, as the amazing "Alex Kidd in Miracle World" game is already built into the system, which allows your adventures with Alex to start as soon as you turn on the power. Of course, the excitement doesn't have to end there – the unit is also compatible with all Master System cartridges, and so the fun goes on...

COMPETITION

We have 3 Sega Master Systems to give away in this great competition. All you have to do to have a chance of winning one is answer these three simple questions:

1 What is the name of Sega's famous blue hedgehog?

2 Who wrote the book *Scouting for Boys*?

3 In which year did the first Scout camp at Brownsea Island take place?

Complete the entry form below and send it to the address shown before 31 January 1995. Send a photocopy or a postcard if you don't want to cut the page. The winners will be the first three correct entries chosen at random after the closing date.

Rules and conditions
1 The competition is open to all United Kingdom Cub Scouts.
2 Prizes are as stated and no cash alternatives will be given.
3 The Editor's decision is final and no correspondence will be entered into.
4 The closing date for receipt of entries is 31 January 1995.

CUB SCOUT SEGA COMPETITION

Write your answers in the spaces provided

Question 1
The name of Sega's famous blue hedgehog is:

....

Question 2
Scouting for Boys was written by:

....

Question 3
The first Scout camp at Brownsea Island took place in:

....

Your name.....................................
Age.........................
Cub Scout Pack..............................
Address......................................
....
....
....
Postcode............................

All entry forms should be returned to the following address:

Sega Competition
1995 Cub Scout Annual
The Scout Association
Baden-Powell House
Queen's Gate
London   SW7 5JS

Don't forget! *The closing date is 31 January 1995.*

SCOUTING AROUND THE WORLD

How many Scouts do you think there are in the world? 5,000 … 50,000 … even 500,000? Well, add about another 24 million and you'd be getting closer as there are over 25 million Scouts in the world today, in over 211 countries.

But what do they do? Are their uniforms the same as ours? Do they have the same badges as us? Let's take a look and see just what Cub Scouts around the world really do get up to!

text: Peter Barker illustrations: Paula Martyr

60

1 United States of America

In the USA, only boys between the ages of 7 and 10 can join the Cubs. When they join at 7, they are called Bobcats. As each boy gets older, he moves on to become a Wolf Cub and then a Bear Cub before moving up into the Scout Troop.
Uniform: blue shirt, blue trousers, a blue and gold scarf and a baseball cap.

2 Mexico

In Mexico, Cub Scouts are called Lobatos and are aged between 8 and 11 years old. Their motto is 'Always my best'. Mexican Cubs enjoy playing games, camping and gaining badges – just like British Cub Scouts really!
Uniform: white shirt, blue shorts and socks, a green cap and a Group scarf.

3 Ghana

Cub Scouts in Ghana are aged between 8 and 11. Ghana is a developing country and Cubs play an important part in helping people and encouraging other children to become Cubs.
Uniform: a green shirt, khaki shorts, a green cap and a yellow scarf.

4 Australia

Australian Cub Scouts work towards their Bronze, Silver and Gold Arrows and take part in many different activities. Camping is a popular activity with Australian Cubs, just as it is with their British counterparts!
Uniform: a short-sleeved khaki shirt (because it is so hot!), khaki shorts, a scarf and a green Cub cap with yellow piping.

5 United Kingdom

British Cub Scouts can be boys or girls aged between 8 and $10\frac{1}{2}$. During their time in the Pack, Cub Scouts will work towards the Adventure and Adventure Crest Award. Many of them will also gain a large number of activity badges for different sports and activities.
Uniform: green sweater, shorts or trousers and a Group scarf.

KNOCK, KNOCK

Knock, knock.
Who's there?
Says.
Says who?
Says me, that's who!

Knock, knock.
Who's there?
Tuba.
Tuba who?
Tuba toothpaste!

Olivier Van den Putte, of the 15th Ealing (Argyle) Pack enjoys steering the narrowboat Twiglet Too through the locks on the Grand Union canal near Northampton.

Although you'll be very busy climbing trees, playing games and enjoying lots of outdoor activities at Camp, there's always time to try out a new hobby – just like this Cub Scout from Heston & Isleworth District.

Knock, knock.
Who's there?
Miss.
Miss who?
Miss L. Toe is nice at Christmas!

Knock, knock.
Who's there?
Della.
Della who?
Della-katessen!

Knock, knock.
Who's there?
Dan.
Dan who?
Dan Druff!

Knock, knock.
Who's there?
Tennis.
Tennis who?
Tennis the sum of five plus five!

Knock, knock.
Who's there?
Lass.
Lass who?
That's what cowboys use, isn't it?